GRANNY and the INDIANS

GRANNY and the INDIANS

by PEGGY PARISH
illustrated by BRINTON TURKLE

The Macmillan Company
Collier-Macmillan Limited, London

The Macmillan Company
Collier-Macmillan Canada, Ltd., Toronto, Ontario

Library of Congress catalog card number: 69-11304

Printed in the United States of America
First Printing

2 7 3 7

for
GLENDORA DONALDSON
with love

Granny Guntry walked along a path
through the woods.

"Those people!" she said.

"Wanting me to move to town.
Telling me the Indians are going
to get me. Pooh! They won't
bother an old lady like me.

And I have my gun.

Of course, it doesn't shoot.

But the Indians don't know that."

Then Granny met a bear. She and

the bear looked at each other.

"One of us has to move,"

said Granny, "and it had

better be you. These are my

good clothes. So go on. Shoo!"

The bear growled at Granny.

"I've no time for nonsense,"

said Granny. And she whacked

the bear across the nose.

That bear moved all right!

And nearby something else moved.

Eyes, Indian eyes, watched Granny.

She didn't see those eyes.

But she did see something else.

"A rabbit trap!" said Granny.

"Maybe there's a rabbit in it.

I do need meat for my stew pot."

Granny went to see. There was a

rabbit in the trap. Granny put
the rabbit in her basket.
And she went on home.
All the time eyes, Indian eyes,
watched her. Then the Indian went
home, too. He told the other
Indians just what had happened.

The next day Granny went
to the woods to pick berries.
She got tired and sat by a
stream to rest. Suddenly a big
fish landed next to her.
The fish flip-flopped all around.
And on one of his flips, he
flopped right into Granny's basket.
"Now how do you like that!"
said Granny. "I was wishing
for some fish!"
Granny didn't see those eyes,
those angry Indian eyes,
watching her. She went on her way.
The Indian went on his way, too.

He told the other Indians
just what had happened.
As Granny was walking along she
heard something in the trees.
She looked up.
There sat a big fat turkey.
"Oh," said Granny, "I do wish
my gun would shoot."
Granny aimed her gun at
the turkey. She pulled the
trigger. And plop!
The turkey hit the ground.
"Well, do tell!" said Granny.
Granny picked up the turkey.
She saw an arrow.

"I don't need that," she said.
She pulled the arrow out and
tossed it away. Granny didn't
see those eyes, those angry
Indian eyes, watching her.
She went on home.
The Indian went home, too.
He told the other Indians
just what had happened.
That night Granny ate turkey.
She ate and ate.
All the while, eyes,
angry Indian eyes, watched her.
Then the Indians went
back to the woods.

"We must do something to stop
Granny Guntry," said the chief.
"She is taking our food."
"We could shoot her,"
said one Indian.

"No! No!" said the chief.
"Then we would have to move or
the townspeople would shoot us.
And I like it here."
"We do have trouble,"
said the Indians.

But Granny had no troubles.
She was just sleepy.
She put a big log on the fire.
And Granny went to bed.

Then Granny heard
that log sputter and pop.
She saw big sparks
fly out of the fireplace.
And Granny wasn't sleepy anymore.

The Indians put another log
on their fire.
But they didn't go to bed.
They had too much to think about.
Suddenly one Indian jumped up.
"Look! Look!" he shouted.
The Indians looked.
They saw a red glow
against the sky.
"Fire!" they said.
"It must be fire!"
The Indians ran to see
what was burning.
"It's Granny Guntry's house!"
said the chief.

"Good! Good!" said all the
Indians. "With no house Granny
will have to move to town.
Then she won't take our food."
The Indians danced and
clapped with joy.
Then they watched the house burn.
Finally with a big swoosh the
house crumbled to the ground.

"Yipee!" shouted the Indians.

"Now we can go home."

"We must celebrate!"
said the chief.

"Yes! Yes!" said the Indians.

And oh, how they celebrated!

Never was there such a pow-wow.

"Our troubles are over!"
they shouted.

But now Granny had troubles,
real troubles. She shook her head.
"My little house is all gone,"
she said. "Whatever will I do?"
Granny thought awhile.

Then she nodded.

"That's it!" she said.

"That's what I'll do."

And Granny headed for the woods.

Granny looked for the Indians.

Finally she saw them.

They saw her, too.

And there were no more
happy shouts.

"Oh, oh," said the chief.

"Trouble is here again."

Granny went to the chief.

"My house burned down," she said.

The chief nodded.

"I'm moving in with you,"

said Granny.

"Oh, no!" said the Indians.

"Oh, yes!" said Granny. "Now you

just go on about your business.

I'll get myself settled."

Those Indians went all right.

Every one of them left the camp.

And they stayed away all day long.

But Granny didn't mind.

"This place is a mess!" she said.

"I'll have to fix that."

And she did.

Finally the Indians returned.

The chief pointed at Granny.

"Go home!" he said.

"I am home!" said Granny.

And she sat herself right down.

Two Indians picked Granny up.

She kicked and screamed.

But those Indians didn't

let her go. They ran through the

woods carrying her.

The other Indians followed.

The Indians ran until they came
to Granny's place. And instead of
a burned-down house there stood
a brand new one.
The Indians dumped Granny inside.

"Now you stay there,"
said the chief.
The Indians turned to go.
But Granny said, "I do like this
house. You deserve a reward.
I'm coming over every day to
cook for you. "
"No! No! No!" said the Indians.
"Oh, it won't be any bother.
I'll eat with you, too,"
said Granny.
"Then I won't have to worry about
meat for my stew pot."
The chief called the
Indians together.

"That woman will decide to be
chief next!" he said.

"No!" said the Indians.

"We must stop her now!"

So the chief turned to Granny.

"You stay here," he said.

"We'll bring you meat."

38

"My, my," said Granny.

"You are good to an old lady.

But there must be something

I can do for you."

"Yes!" said the Indians.

"Stay out of our woods.

We might shoot you yet."

That's what Granny did.

And every day she found meat for
her stew pot by the door.
Every day Granny said, "I could
do a lot for those Indians. I'll
tell them so when I see them."
But Granny never saw the Indians.
They made sure of that.